The Story of Maggie and Early BFF

Sheila Derreberry

Illustrations by Blueberry Illustrations

This book is dedicated with love to my daughter Lisa, son-in-law Jack, my two youngest grandchildren Mason and Emme, and of course Maggie and Early. Without each of them, the sharing of this story would not have happened. Please read it to your children with lots of energy and expression and enjoy!

In loving memory of Maggie (August 15, 2008–December 18, 2019).

Sheila Derreberry

At some point in in-life's journey most of us come to the realization that the true meaning of life is about who you are as a human being. It is not about things acquired but rather about matters of the heart, love for others, and selfless acts of kindness as taught in God's Word. These generally are also the traits we see in children and the same characteristics that bring true peace of mind. One thing that inspired this book, which is based on true events, is the joy and laughter that I saw in the faces of my grandchildren as they played tirelessly with Maggie and Early. Also, the ways in which they tried to deal with the ultimate loss of Maggie really stirred my emotions. After Maggie passed away, 5-year-old Mason asked his mother if she knew of anyone who was going to die soon. Not thinking about his reasoning, she told him she didn't know and wanted to know why he was asking. He said that if she knew of someone, then he wanted to write a letter for Maggie and send it with them. Emme, 3 years old, told her mother a few days later that she had prayed the night before and had asked God if He would bring Maggie back from the "died land." To be so small, I think these comments exemplify the sensitivity and unconditional love present in children whether for pets, family, friends, or anyone. In Matthew 19:14, Jesus says to allow the little children to come unto Him, for "of such is the Kingdom of Heaven."
What a better world this would be if each of us would put into practice the heartfelt love and forgiving attitude as seen in a child.

From the first day they met, Maggie Susan and Early Rider were the best of friends! Early proudly strutted around, and so he should, as he was tall and square-jawed and sported a beautifully brindle-colored coat with perfect inflections of white and black. Then there was Maggie who was a friendly black Labrador, quite sassy-looking and adorned with a shiny black coat that was as black as the blackest night. Almost always she appeared to be flashing a bright, white smile at you. Maggie would be a little ornery and sneaky like a cat at times. When caught doing something that she shouldn't be doing, she would strike the most innocent look on her face, as if to say, "What?" or "Who, me?" She loved everyone and just knew everyone loved her even if they were not dog lovers. One day she saw a neighbor across the street. Always longing for a treat or to be petted on top of the head, she innocently took off running right toward him, wagging her tail all the way. He, on the other hand, saw this completely strange dog wildly approaching him and took off running down the street like a race horse, as she scared the daylights out of him! Maggie could not at all understand his reaction. Of the two canines, Early was definitely the calmer and more obedient one; Maggie, not so much, but oh was she ever a barrel of fun!

We probably should go back and introduce their masters so you can know just how Maggie and Early first met. Maggie Susan belonged to Lisa, and Early Rider belonged to Jack. Lisa was just out of college and unknowingly was about to meet her future husband at her new job. Yes, Jack was employed at the very same school! They began spending time talking, and eventually started to date. This was only the beginning for them and what would soon become an ever-binding friendship for Maggie and Early. When Jack would come to visit Lisa he would bring Early. Sometimes the four of them would go for a walk. Early would get so excited when he would see Maggie. The two dogs would run and play for hours! If there was a nearby creek, they would dart toward it and jump in, no matter how muddy the water! These doggies were not about to miss a perfect opportunity for a nice cool swim!

There were a few times when Jack would come to Lisa's house without Early, and Maggie would be so very sad. They literally would sometimes appear to cry if they had to leave each other. Jack soon decided he needed to bring Early every time he came, no matter what! The dogs were quickly becoming very close to each other, very much like a brother and sister! When Jack and Lisa wanted to go out alone they would put the dog kennels side by side, which made the dogs as happy as could be as long as they could just see each other and be close together. Every now and then you could even catch them kissing each other through the openings in the kennels!

Along with all the fun times though, quite often came very trying times! Jack had once written a very important paper for a school assignment, and it was his only copy. Without thinking, he laid it on the sofa for just a moment, and all of a sudden there sat Maggie with shreds of the school paper dangling from her teeth! No doubt that she was the culprit. If you scolded her for anything though, she would run and hide under a table or behind the sofa. She thought that if she could not see anyone, then no one could see her! If you could not see her, then of course you couldn't be angry, right?

Maggie ate everything and I do mean EVERYTHING! Once Lisa's mom came to visit. After entering the room, she set her partially opened purse on the floor, which later turned out to be a bad move. Maggie lurked closer and closer toward the purse while everyone was talking.

And there it was—a crisp dollar bill sticking out of the purse just enough so that Maggie could grab it and take off. The more we chased her, the harder she ran! By the time we caught her, she had already chomped up half the dollar bill! Stuffed toys, metal screws, frisbees, rocks, socks, earplugs—you name anything and Maggie had either eaten it or had made a gallant attempt to do so!

And, oh, I almost forgot—
Maggie loved to eat bugs.
She delighted in catching
seasonal cicadas, while
they were still in flight I
might add, and you guessed
it again, chomp, chomp,
chomp—down the hatch
they would go! Once when
Maggie saw Lisa upset,
she ran to the hamper and
quickly gulped down a pair
of underwear! Can you
believe it? Remember I told
you she was kind of sneaky,
much like a cat. Once when

Lisa's mom baked a cake and turned her back for just a few minutes, Maggie saw her chance. She ambled into the kitchen, jumped up to the counter, and helped herself to a very big portion of the freshly baked cake!

The veterinarian of course quite quickly learned all about Maggie and would see her regularly. She knew her on a first-name basis, mind you, and over time she had to perform quite a few X-rays at the office to see why poor Maggie wasn't feeling well. The doctor once discovered not one but two full-size socks in Maggie's belly! Another time she discovered a half-eaten tennis ball! Oh, brother! Upon learning all about Maggie's constant tendency to get into trouble, it may make you question whether or not you would even want a dog like her. However, if you only once saw how far and how fast Maggie would run to catch a frisbee or a tennis ball and rarely miss, you would have taken her without even thinking twice— mischievous nature and all!

Maggie could give you high fives and do all the usual doggie tricks, but she loved to play catch more than anything! Early, on the other hand, would much rather relax along the sidelines. He was not so big on competitive events that required a lot of physical exertion. Don't

get me wrong. Early would occasionally try to run and grab sticks
or frisbees from Maggie just to prove that he too could be skillful,
if and when he wanted to be, that is. He also loved swimming with
her and going for walks, but mostly Early was quite content to get a
good belly rub now and then and just watch Maggie.

I almost forgot to tell you that Maggie was a bit of a scaredy-cat when it came to two things—storms and vacuums, or actually anything small and motorized. One night when she was sleeping on the floor by Lisa's bed, a big clap of thunder boomed and Maggie leapt straight up just as if she had been shot from a cannon! She was so very relieved to land in that safe, warm bed with Lisa! On another day, we took Maggie for a walk and happened to come near a gentleman in a motorized chair. He was attempting to back up and give us a clear path, but Maggie apparently thought he was driving deliberately right at her. Completely terrified, she flipped in the air, while still on her leash I might add! Poor Maggie. Needless to say, we had to cross the street to continue our walk.

Well, Lisa and Jack continued to date and one cold wintry day Jack proposed to Lisa and they got married the following summer! Maggie and Early were so happy. Now they could be together all the time! Just like a brother and sister, the doggies would occasionally get a little jealous of each other if they felt one was getting more attention than the other. If Early would go lay down at Jack's feet, then Maggie would slink over to Early and ever so gently clamp her teeth around Early's collar, tugging at him trying desperately to move him away from Jack. Early reluctantly would get up but then would turn right around returning to his spot and politely sit down right on top of Maggie's head! YIKES! Imagine someone pinning your head down and putting an 80-pound weight on it!

Maggie was quite the entertainer. She literally would lay on her back, stretch her head to one side, pick up a ball in her mouth, hold her paws to her mouth, take the ball out, hold it up to look at it, and then put it back in her mouth! Who would not love to have a dog like that?

Maggie's human grandmother, known as "Nana," was referred to as the treat lady to the dogs, and oh how much did Maggie and Early love to see her! Nana went to the park one day with Lisa. Maggie was

running her usual laps and jumping through the stationary hoops. On seeing Nana, all of a sudden, she veered and ran toward her like a speeding bullet! Oh, no! Yes, you guessed it—Maggie crashed right into Nana's knees and down she went. Her legs flew up in the air and boom! Down on her back she fell right into the cold wet snow! Oh, my!

Well, as time passed, along came two new additions to this happy household. Mason was born first, and then Emme. Maggie and Early didn't quite know how to react to these new little creatures. Secretly, I think they may have been afraid that the children would one day take their place. But, oh, how wrong they were! They soon figured out that with Mason and Emme, that just meant two more people to play with them and love them. When the kids would get their swimming pool out in summertime, there went Maggie, stepping right into the pool as if it was placed out there for her instead of the children.

One day when the kids were at school, Maggie and Early saw an opportunity to slip out of their yard and go on a neighborhood adventure just to see what they could find. They weren't doing anything wrong, but just wanted to go for an innocent walk. The problem arose when Maggie either got tired or thirsty, and there she went again.

A neighbor had left his patio door open. Maggie just trotted right into the man's house and laid down on his kitchen floor! Imagine his surprise! He must have known that Maggie meant no harm though, as he took her picture and posted it with the headline "Does anyone know this dog?" Yes, there was Maggie's picture looking just as happy as she could be. Of course, Lisa was shocked when she saw that picture! She had to go retrieve the dogs and get them back to their own yard before they got into any more mischief! In Maggie's defense though, the patio door WAS wide open!

As goes the circle of life, the years passed by, and Maggie grew older and started feeling very tired. She would still try to run and play but just did not have the energy anymore. Even the animal doctor could not make her well again. The last time Maggie went to the doctor, her whole family went with her for they knew that this time she would not be able to come back home. They will miss her forever but Maggie is not sick anymore, and that makes them very happy. Early can only dream of his beloved friend now. But I am sure that every time he thinks of her, he remembers all the fun adventures they had and pictures his furry partner playing catch with tennis balls and frisbees, swimming, and running like the wind! Yes indeed, Maggie and Early were quite the pair, and definitely in his mind, best friends forever!

I grew up in a modest home with little from the standpoint of material items but felt so fortunate to have had the most loving, devoted parents and caring sisters that anyone could hope to have. By God's grace, this journey in life later afforded my husband and me the amazing honor of rearing a son and daughter whose importance in my life is inexpressible and for whom my love cannot be measured. I've also known the joy of a close relationship with each of my four precious grandchildren who are in a word, priceless. Most of my working life has been spent in the field of finance. I enjoy movies, games, cooking, and spending time with my family and friends. I've never felt deserving of anything, only gratitude as I have been blessed abundantly by my Creator. I know I cannot repay Him, especially for the ultimate gift of His only Son, but I try to do my best to live for God and to give Him the glory and honor that He deserves.

Sheila Derreberry

CPSIA information can be obtained
at www.ICGtesting.com
Printed in the USA
BVHW021217230820
587090BV00026B/339